S0-BOA-186

**Scott, Foresman
Basics in Reading**

Calico Caper

Program Authors

Ira E. Aaron
Dauris Jackson
Carole Riggs
Richard G. Smith
Robert Tierney

Book Authors

Robert E. Jennings
Dorothy E. Prince

**Instructional
Consultant**

John Manning

Scott, Foresman and Company
Editorial Offices: Glenview, Illinois

Regional Sales Offices: Palo Alto, California •
Tucker, Georgia • Glenview, Illinois •
Oakland, New Jersey • Dallas, Texas

Consultants

May Arakaki

Maria Eugenia Matute-Bianchi

Maria Bilbao

Delphina B. Briscoe

Deborah Flores

Jesse Garcia

Evangeline Geiger

Gordon Gray

Barbara Griffin

Barbara Hansen

Jerry A. Rainwater

Betty Robeson

Ann Semel

Joan Takada

Michiko Ikegami Totman

Evelynn Washington

Acknowledgments

page 64: John H. Gerard

page 74 bottom: Tony Ray Jones, MAGNUM PHOTOS

page 75 bottom: Dr. Frank Maglione

ISBN 0-673-11406-6

Copyright © 1978,
Scott, Foresman and Company, Glenview, Illinois.
All Rights Reserved.
Printed in the United States of America.

12345678910-KPH-858483828180797877

Contents

Section One

Section Two

Section One

Look and Listen

»Most consonant letters stand for one sound.
But watch out for *c* and *g*.
Two consonant letters together usually
stand for two sounds.
But watch out for *sh*, *th*, and *ch*. «

1. book   robin   tub

2. cup   circle   gate   giraffe

3. flag   skate   cart   stamp

4. ship   thimble   chicken

1: Teach

potato chips

ice cream

pickles

gum

candy

mustard

cheese

hamburger

milk

1. Which things begin like *me?*
2. Which things end like *am?*
3. Which thing has the m sound in the middle?
4. Does the *c* in *ice* sound like the *c* in *cream?*
5. Which things have the k sound?
6. Which things have the ch sound?
7. Which could you put on a hamburger?

1. Which things on the list are in
   the picture?
2. What are all the things on the list?

        meat   fruit

Practice skills

1. Which things on the list are in
   the picture?
2. What are all the things on the list?

        sweets   fruit

10

Mikey Helps

Dad and the children went to the store.
Dad gave a list to Stacy.

"Find the things on your list, Stacy,"
Dad said.
"Put them in the cart.
I'll get the things on my list."

Mikey held out his hand for a list.
But Dad didn't see him.

Stacy went one way.
Dad went another.
He pushed the cart.
Mikey went with him.

1: Appl

Dad saw Mr. Gomez.
Dad and Mr. Gomez talked.
They walked up and down the rows.

Dad put things into the cart.
Mikey took things out of the cart.

Stacy put things into the cart.
Mikey took things out of the cart.
Then Stacy came with the pickles.

"Look, Dad," Stacy said.
"There's nothing in the cart.
And where is Mikey?"

Dad and Stacy found Mikey.
Mikey was putting things away.

"Oh, Mikey," said Dad.
"You want to help, don't you?
I'll give you my list."

Dad put Mikey in the cart.
He gave Mikey a list to hold.
Then Stacy and Dad went to find the
things again.

Think about the selection

1. Why do you think Mikey held out his hand for a list?
2. How do you think Mikey felt when he didn't get a list?
3. Find something someone said in the story. Be ready to read it.

Checkpoint 1

Look at the lists.

1. Which things begin like *bring*?
2. Which thing ends like *am*?
3. Which thing has the m sound in the middle?
4. Which things have the k sound?
5. Does the *c* in *lettuce* sound like the *c* in *cake*?
6. Which things are not food?

16

Life on a Ranch

This is a big ranch.
It has lots of land.

There are cattle on the ranch.
There are sheep too.

The sheep need much care.
The cattle need much care.
Many people help.

Some people ride horses.
They watch the animals.

Sometimes the animals get away.
This man uses a rope to
catch one.
The rope is called a lasso.

This pickup truck brings some food for
the animals.

Sometimes the truck breaks down.
This woman fixes it.

All the people on a ranch work hard.

Think about the selection
1. What are sheep and cattle?
    toys   animals   trucks
2. What is a lasso?
    a ranch   a rope   a horse

2 The Word Breaker

Context
Root words
Endings
Contractions
Compounds

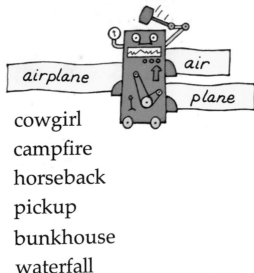

cowgirl

campfire

horseback

pickup

bunkhouse

waterfall

hasn't

let's

can't

you're

haven't

I'll

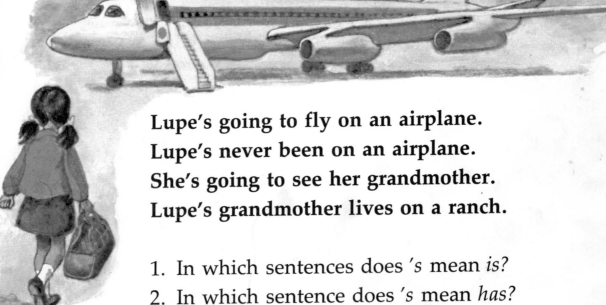

Lupe's going to fly on an airplane.
Lupe's never been on an airplane.
She's going to see her grandmother.
Lupe's grandmother lives on a ranch.

1. In which sentences does *'s* mean *is?*
2. In which sentence does *'s* mean *has?*

22

A cowboy is meeting Lupe. He's bringing Grandmother's pickup truck.

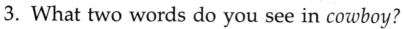

3. What two words do you see in *cowboy?*
4. What two words do you see in *pickup?*
5. In which word does *'s* mean *is?*

Practice skills

There's a bunkhouse
at Grandmother's ranch.

1. In which word does *'s* mean *is?*
2. What is a bunkhouse?
    - a house for birds
    - a bed
    - a house with bunk beds

GRANDMOTHER'S SURPRISE

2: Apply

The airplane came to a stop.
Lupe walked down the steps.
She didn't see Grandmother.
She hadn't visited Grandmother for
a year.
But Lupe was sure she'd know
Grandmother.

"Hi, partner," said a cowboy.
"Good to see you again."

Lupe looked up.
It was Tumbleweed.
He was a cowboy on her
grandmother's ranch.

26

Lupe and Tumbleweed got in the
pickup truck.
Down the road they went.
They stopped in front of a store.

"Grandmother," cried Lupe.
"I'm here!"

"Oh, Lupe," said Grandmother.
"I'm glad to see you."

28

Grandmother took a good look at Lupe.
She looked at Lupe from head to toe.

"I bought a surprise for you,"
said Grandmother.
"But I'm the one who's surprised."

Grandmother took some clothes out of
a bag.
She held them up to Lupe.

"I guess these clothes would have fit
  you last year," Grandmother said.
"Come on, Lupe.
  Let's go into the store.
  We'll take these clothes back.
  We'll get some things to fit you now."

Think about the selection

1. Who met Lupe at the airplane?
2. Where was Grandmother waiting for Lupe?
3. Why did Grandmother take the clothes back?

Checkpoint 2 ▮▮▮▮▮▮▮▮▮▮▮▮

Lupe stayed at Grandmother's ranch all summer.
She learned to ride horseback.
She helped make campfires.
Lupe says she's going to be a cowgirl when she grows up.

1. In which word does *'s* mean *is*?
2. What two words are in each word?
   horseback   campfires   cowgirl

3

What Is It?

**Take two pieces
of bread.**

**Put peanut butter
on one piece.**

**Put the other
piece on top.**

**Now you have
a sandwich.**

Think about skills

You can use parts to make things.
Bread and peanut butter are parts.
1. What do they make?

Here are some parts.

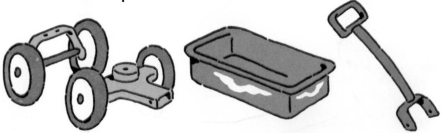

2. What thing could these parts make?
If you said "a wagon," you were right.

32

3. What thing could the parts above make?
sandwich   hamburger   birthday cake

Practice skills

1. What thing could the parts above make?

balloon   kite   campfire

How Taffy Apples Are Made

Taffy apples are made from apples, sticks,
taffy, and nuts. Let's see how.

3: Apply

The apples come in boxes.
Some apples are too big.
Some apples are too small.
A machine picks out the right apples.

One woman puts in the sticks.
The sticks must be tight.

A man watches the taffy.
It must be just hot enough.

This machine dips the
apples in taffy.

While the taffy is hot, these people roll
the apples in nuts.

Then the taffy apples go to
the store.
You can buy taffy apples in
the store.

These children like taffy apples. Do you?

3: Apply

Think about the selection

1. How do machines help make taffy apples?
   a. A machine dips apples in taffy.
   b. A machine puts sticks in the apples.
   c. A machine picks the right apples.
2. On page 36, what does *it* stand for?
   a. the sticks
   b. a man
   c. the taffy
3. What happens first? next? last?
   a. Apples are dipped in taffy.
   b. Apples are rolled in nuts.
   c. Sticks are put in apples.

Checkpoint 3

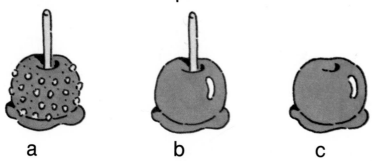

1. What could the parts above make?

   a   b   c

First, Next, Last

Pat put a seed in some dirt.
She watered it every day.
The seed grew into a plant.

Think about skills
In the story things happened in a
certain order.
First Pat put a seed in dirt.
Next she watered the seed.
Last the seed grew into a plant.

Sometimes you can look at pictures and
tell the order in which
things happened.

a

b

c

Look at the pictures.
1. What happened first? next? last?

4: Teach

Amy helped Dad
make a cake.
Then Amy tasted it.

"This cake tastes good,"
said Amy.

Dad said, "I'm
glad you like it.
Now we'll do the dishes."

1. What happened first? next? last?
   a. Amy tasted the cake.
   b. Dad said, "Now we'll do the dishes."
   c. Amy helped Dad make a cake.

  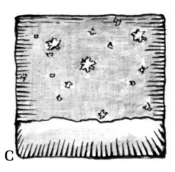

a   b   c

Look at the pictures.
2. What happened first? next? last?

Debbie Duck

by Sallie Ann Rowe

Once there was a little duck named Debbie.
Every day Debbie and her mother went to
the pond.

Debbie's mother would swim in the water.
Debbie would sit in the warm sand.

4: Apply

One day Debbie's mother called, "Debbie!
It's time to swim."

Debbie put her foot in the water.

"This water is wet and cold," she said.

"Yes, Debbie," said her mother. "It is."

"I don't like it," said Debbie.
"I'm not going to swim."

"But all ducks swim," said her mother.

"Not this duck," said Debbie.
Then she sat down on a pile of sand.

Every day Debbie's mother would swim.
Every day Debbie would sit in the sand.

4: Apply

One day Debbie's mother called,
"Look out, Debbie. I see a big cat."

Debbie saw the cat. It was a big cat.
It was bigger than Debbie.

"Run fast," called her mother.
Debbie ran fast.

"Slide," called her mother.
Debbie slid into the water. SPLASH!

4: Apply

Debbie swam to her mother.

"You're safe now," said her mother.
"The cat won't get us here.
Cats don't like water."

"I'm glad ducks do," said Debbie.

Think about the selection

1. Could this story have happened?
2. Find something Debbie's mother said. Be ready to read it.
3. When did Debbie swim in the pond?

Checkpoint 4

1. What happened first? next? last?

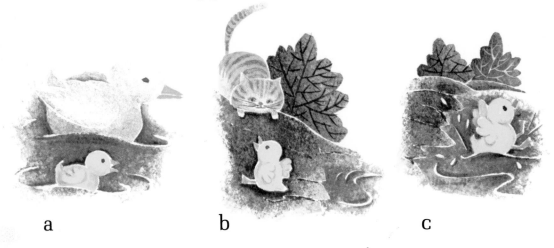

a   b   c

2. What did Debbie's mother say first? next? last?
   a. She told Debbie, "Run fast."
   b. She told Debbie, "Slide."
   c. She told Debbie, "I see a big cat."

A Flower Pot Is Not a Hat

by Martha Moffett

A flower pot is not a hat.
If I put it on my head,
it is my hat.

From *A Flower Pot Is Not a Hat* by Martha Moffett, illustrated by Susan Perl. Copyright © 1972 by Martha Moffet and Susan Perl. Reprinted by permission of the publishers, E. P. Dutton and Charles Neighbors, Inc.

An empty box is not a drum.
If I pound on it, it is my drum.

A park bench is not a horse.
If I ride on it, it is my horse.

A laundry basket is not a bed.
If I sleep in it, it is my bed.

If I can pound on it, ride on it, and sleep in it—

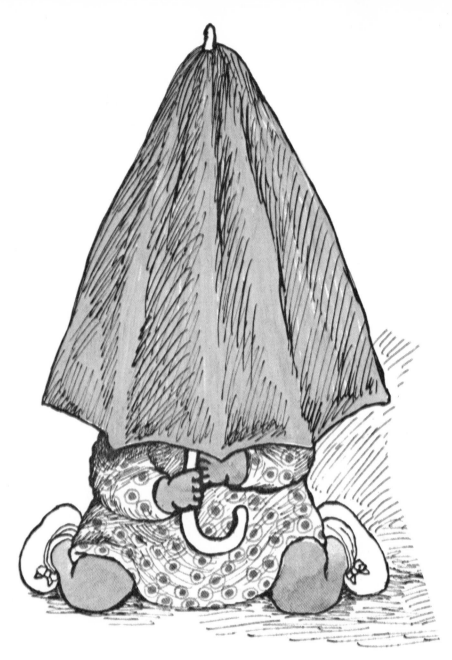

and if I can put it on my head—then I can
say what it is.

Think about the selection

1. What did a child use for a hat?

   flower pot   bench   laundry basket

2. What else could you use for a hat?

3. What did a child use for a bed?

   drum   flower pot   laundry basket

4. What else could you use for a bed?

5. What could you use these things for?

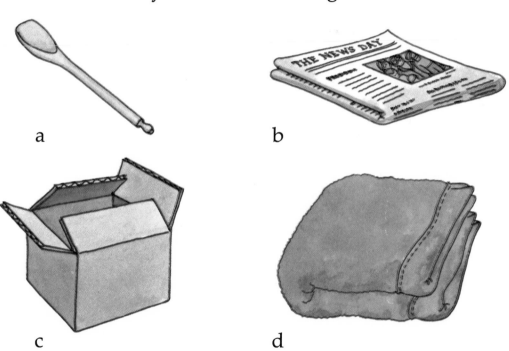

a

b

c

d

5

Hope Helps

The letters *a* and *o* are vowel letters.

»A vowel letter stands for more than one sound.**«**

It was dark on the farm.
Hope had to wake up.
She washed her face.
She drank milk and ate.
She went to the barn.

You saw these words.

dark	had	wake
farm	drank	face

Hope got a bone for the dog.
She gave the hens lots
of corn.
Then Hope heard a horn.
It was a school bus.

You saw these words.

corn	got	Hope
for	lots	bone

5: Teach

Words like *dark* and *corn* usually have an
r-controlled vowel sound.
Words like *had* and *got* usually have a
short vowel sound.
Words like *wake* and *bone* usually have a
long vowel sound.

farm　　drank　　face　　for　　lots　　Hope

1. Which words have r-controlled
   vowel sounds?
2. Which words have short vowel sounds?
3. Which words have long vowel sounds?

Practice skills

Jane was Hope's little sister.
She watered the rose by
the porch.
She did not water the
grass in the yard.

porch　　not　　Jane　　yard　　grass　　rose

1. Which words have r-controlled sounds?
2. Which words have short sounds?
3. Which words have long sounds?

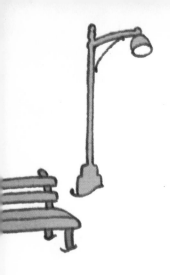

A Hat for Me

by Anne Runck

It was winter.
An ape, a fox, and a bear went to the park.
The ape and the fox liked to skate.
But the bear said it was not his sport.
He just sat on a rock.

58

The ape and the fox found a hat.

"My hat is at home," said the ape.
"I need this hat."

"My hat is at home," said the fox.
"I need this hat."

The ape grabbed the hat.
The fox grabbed the hat too.
They started to pull.
They pulled and pulled.
The hat got bigger and bigger.

"You will make the hat too big for
me," said the fox.
But the ape pulled and pulled.

"You will make the hat too big for
me," said the ape.
But the fox pulled and pulled.

Just then the ape slipped.
So did the fox. They sat down hard.

The hat flew out of their hands.
It flew across the ice.

It landed on the bear's head.
"What a joke," said the bear.
"It's a hat for me. It's just my size."

Think about the selection

1. Who found the hat?
2. Who wanted the hat?
3. Who got the hat? How?
4. Could this story have happened?
5. What are the ape, the fox, and the bear?

   sheep   animals   birds

Checkpoint 5

home	hat	for	rock
and	skate	hard	ape
fox	joke	sport	park

1. Which words have r-controlled vowel sounds?
2. Which words have short vowel sounds?
3. Which words have long vowel sounds?

Bonus
Selection

Butterflies

by Sara Booth

Butterflies are flying up and down
fly up to the sky and to the ground.
Butterflies are dancing all around
flutter, flutter, flutter not a sound.

''Butterflies'' by Sara Booth from *The Weewish Tree*, May 1976.
Copyright © 1976 by the American Indian Historical Society.
Reprinted by permission.

Look and Listen

The letters *i, u,* and *e* are vowel letters.
» A vowel letter stands for more than
one sound. «

1. First Alma had five small fish.
   Then she got six pet mice.
   five   fish   first

2. Bruce has a cute cat, Muff.
   Muff sleeps on a fake fur rug.
   Bruce   Muff   fur

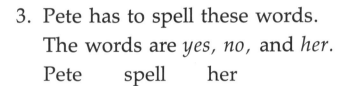

3. Pete has to spell these words.
   The words are *yes, no,* and *her.*
   Pete   spell   her

Words like *five, Bruce,* and *Pete* usually
have a long vowel sound.
Words like *fish, Muff,* and *spell* usually
have a short vowel sound.
Words like *first, fur,* and *her* usually
have an r-controlled vowel sound.
The letters *ir, ur,* and *er* usually
stand for the same r-controlled sound.

Steve went to a <u>pet</u> shop.
He saw a <u>bird</u> <u>jump</u> on a <u>perch</u>.
He saw a <u>cute</u> dog <u>with</u> <u>curls</u>.
Steve thought the pets were <u>nice</u>.

1. Which underlined words have r-controlled vowel sounds?
2. Which underlined words have short vowel sounds?
3. Which underlined words have long vowel sounds?

Practice skills

This <u>girl</u> is Jo.
She couldn't <u>use</u> <u>her</u> <u>bike</u>.
The wheel didn't <u>turn</u> <u>left</u>.
<u>But</u> she got tools from <u>Pete</u> to <u>fix</u> it.

1. Which underlined words have r-controlled vowel sounds?
2. Which underlined words have short vowel sounds?
3. Which underlined words have long vowel sounds?

The Big Bike

by Sallie Ann Rowe

Kim had a new bike.
It was her first big bike.
It was so big that it was hard to ride.

Kim wanted to ride.
But she kept falling.
One day Kim fell in the dirt.
She hit her head.

"Kim," said her mother, "that bike is too big
for you to use.
I may have to put it away until you
get bigger."

"I'm OK, Mom," said Kim.
"Maybe next time I won't fall."

Just then Kim's brother Gene came home.
Kim asked him something.
Gene began to smile. Kim smiled too.

The next day Kim's friends came over.
They wanted her to go for a bike ride.

"I don't think you should go," said
her mother. "You might fall again."

"But I won't get hurt this time," said Kim.

Kim ran into the house. Soon she came out.
She said, "Now I won't get hurt if I fall."

Think about the selection

1. What did Kim want to do with her friends?
2. What was Kim's problem?
3. How did Gene help Kim?

Checkpoint 6

like	just	use
next	Gene	dirt
her	hurt	big

1. Which words have r-controlled vowel sounds?
2. Which words have short vowel sounds?
3. Which words have long vowel sounds?

72

Wheels

Some wheels are big.
You can ride on this wheel.

73

Some wheels are small.
You can have fun
with these wheels.

Wheels help you do things you can't do by yourself.

Wheels make life easier.
Wheels make life more fun.

Think about the selection

1. How can wheels make life easier?

2. How can wheels make life more fun?

Section One Checkpoint

Word Identification Tests

Subtest 1

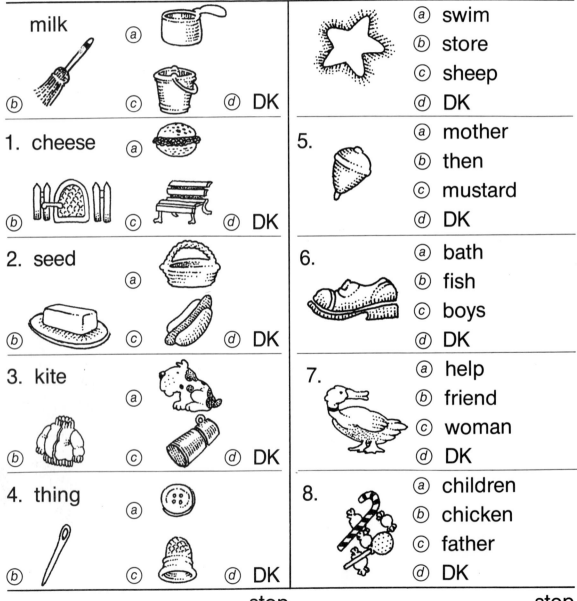

milk
Ⓒ a
Ⓑ b   Ⓓ c   Ⓕ DK

Ⓒ a swim
Ⓑ b store
Ⓓ c sheep
Ⓕ DK

1. cheese
Ⓒ a
Ⓑ b   Ⓓ c   Ⓕ DK

5.
Ⓒ a mother
Ⓑ b then
Ⓓ c mustard
Ⓕ DK

2. seed
Ⓒ a
Ⓑ b   Ⓓ c   Ⓕ DK

6.
Ⓒ a bath
Ⓑ b fish
Ⓓ c boys
Ⓕ DK

3. kite
Ⓒ a
Ⓑ b   Ⓓ c   Ⓕ DK

7.
Ⓒ a help
Ⓑ b friend
Ⓓ c woman
Ⓕ DK

4. thing
Ⓒ a
Ⓑ b   Ⓓ c   Ⓕ DK

8.
Ⓒ a children
Ⓑ b chicken
Ⓓ c father
Ⓕ DK

stop   stop

Subtest 2

short 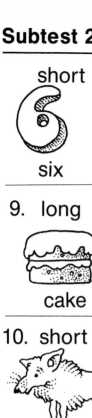 six	ⓐ slide ⓑ girl ⓒ stick ⓓ DK	

9. long 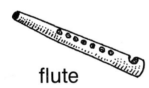 cake	ⓐ flag ⓑ skate ⓒ yard ⓓ DK	

13. r-controlled

ⓐ park
ⓑ hat
ⓒ ape
ⓓ DK

10. short

fox
ⓐ hope
ⓑ short
ⓒ pot
ⓓ DK

14. short

ⓐ turn
ⓑ use
ⓒ fun
ⓓ DK

11. long

flute
ⓐ cute
ⓑ just
ⓒ truck
ⓓ DK

15. r-controlled

ⓐ rope
ⓑ sport
ⓒ rock
ⓓ DK

12. short
elf
ⓐ these
ⓑ wet
ⓒ her
ⓓ DK

16. long
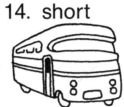
ⓐ first
ⓑ time
ⓒ swim
ⓓ DK

17. r-controlled

ⓐ farm
ⓑ fur
ⓒ corn
ⓓ DK

stop

Pedro saw Julie on the hill.
Julie called, "I have a new sled.
It's larger than my old one."

Pedro said, "I have my
brother's sled.
It's been fun using it.
Let's race downhill."

18. In which sentence does 's mean *is*?
    ⓐ I have my brother's sled.
    ⓑ It's larger than my old one.
    ⓒ Let's race downhill.   ⓓ DK

19. In which sentence does 's mean *has*?
    ⓐ It's been fun using it.
    ⓑ It's larger than my old one.
    ⓒ Let's race downhill.   ⓓ DK

20. Which word has two words put
    together to make a new word?
    ⓐ called
    ⓑ brother
    ⓒ downhill   ⓓ DK

stop

Subtest 4

21.	ⓐ bread	ⓑ back		25.	ⓐ selection	ⓑ school
	ⓒ book	ⓓ DK			ⓒ sentence	ⓓ DK
22.	ⓐ color	ⓑ call		26.	ⓐ time	ⓑ them
	ⓒ cold	ⓓ DK			ⓒ turn	ⓓ DK
23.	ⓐ from	ⓑ four		27.	ⓐ when	ⓑ wheel
	ⓒ flag	ⓓ DK			ⓒ woman	ⓓ DK
24.	ⓐ me	ⓑ many		28.	ⓐ would	ⓑ your
	ⓒ men	ⓓ DK			ⓒ who	ⓓ DK

Possible Word Identification Score: 28   **stop**

Comprehension Tests

Subtest 5

1. A *flagpole* is a
   ⓐ pole for a flag
   ⓑ flag on a pole
   ⓒ DK

2. A *birdhouse* is a
   ⓐ bird on a house
   ⓑ house for birds
   ⓒ DK

3. *Lots* of candy is
   ⓐ much candy
   ⓑ some candy
   ⓒ DK

4. *To grab* means
   ⓐ to give
   ⓑ to take
   ⓒ DK

stop

Subtest 6

Here are some parts.

5. What thing could these parts make?

ⓐ wall clock   ⓑ alarm clock   ⓒ watch   ⓓ DK

Here are some parts.

6. What thing could these parts make?

  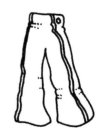

ⓐ jacket   ⓑ jump suit   ⓒ slacks   ⓓ DK

Section Two

All Fall Down

**Nan set up
her blocks.
She pushed
just one.
All the blocks
fell down.**

Think about skills

1. Why did all the blocks fall down?

Did you say it was because Nan pushed
a block? If you did, you were right.

**Sam's baby brother was crying.
Dad fixed a bottle for the baby.
Sam gave his brother the bottle.
Then his brother was happy.**

2. Why did the baby cry?
3. What made the baby happy?

Pete was Sue's pet bird.
Sue wanted Pete to talk.
So she said "Pretty Pete" over and over.
Then one day Pete said "Pretty Pete" too.

4. Why did Sue say "Pretty Pete" to the bird?

Practice skills

Pablo blew up
a balloon.
It got bigger
and bigger.
Pablo let the
balloon go.
The air
rushed out.
The balloon flew.

1. What made the balloon get bigger and bigger?
2. What made the balloon fly?

Marla's Plan

Tom and Ben dry the dishes.
They take turns.
They can't always remember whose turn it is.

86

One day Tom wrote a
letter to Marla.

Dear Marla,
     The children dry the
dishes at our house.   There
are lots of dishes and
glasses to dry. There are
pots and pans too.
     Ben and I take
turns. But we can't
always remember whose
turn it is. Sometimes
we fight.
     Can you help us?

                    Your friend,
                    Tom

Tom took the letter to the mailbox.

Marla got Tom's letter.
She opened it.

Marla thought about the problem.

She saw a calendar.

She got an idea.

Then Marla sent a letter to Tom.

Dear Tom,
    One week you can dry the dishes. The next week Ben can dry.
    You and Ben can mark off the weeks on a calendar.
    I hope this plan works.

    Your friend,
    Marla

Think about the selection

1. What was Tom's problem?
2. What did Marla tell Tom to do?
3. Find the word *mailbox* on page 88.
   What two words do you see in *mailbox?*

Checkpoint 7

1. Why did Tom write to Marla?
   a. Tom took turns with Ben.
   b. Tom had a problem.

2. Why did Marla write to Tom?
   a. Marla had a problem.
   b. Marla had an idea.

A Letter for Sako

SAKO YONEYAME
623 MAPLE ST.
EVANSTON, ILLINOIS
60201

Fran wrote this letter.
It was for her friend Sako.

Fran took the letter to the
mailbox.
She put the letter into
the box.

Someone came from the
post office.
He opened the box.
He took out all the letters.

The letters went into a big bag.
So did the letter for Sako.
The bag went into the truck.

All the letters went to the post office.
Many people work there.
They help the letters go to the
right places.

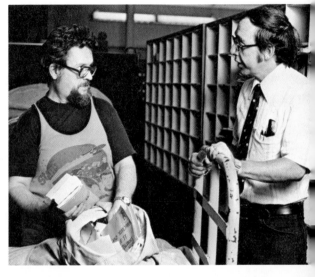

The letter for Sako went into a bag.
The bag was put into another truck.
This truck went near Sako's house.

This mail carrier took the bag off the truck.

The mail carrier went to Sako's house.
He gave the letter to Sako.

Think about the selection

1. Who sent a letter to Sako?
2. Where did the letter go first? next? last?
    a. to Sako's house
    b. into the mailbox
    c. to the post office

My Grandpa

I wanted to play ball.
So Grandpa said he would teach me.
He is teaching me to bat and catch.

I bat the ball.
Grandpa runs and catches it.
Then Grandpa bats the ball to me.

We have not played ball very long.
I hope Grandpa teaches me to run and
slide too.
I want to go on playing ball.
I want to play ball as well as
my grandpa does.

» Letters can be added at the end of words to make new words.
The letters s, *es*, *ed*, *ing* are endings.
The words to which endings are added are root words. **«**

You saw these words in the story.

play	catch	bat
played	catches	bats
playing		

The words *play*, *catch*, and *bat* are root words.
The other words are root words with endings.

1. What endings were added to *play*?
2. What ending was added to *catch*?
3. What ending was added to *bat*?

You saw these words in the story too.

wanted	teach	runs
want	teaching	run
	teaches	

4. Which words are root words?
5. Which endings were added to the root words?

Mom and Dad
both work.
Dad <u>works</u> at
a school.
He <u>teaches</u>
second grade.
Mom is a
police officer.

We all work at home at night.
I change the <u>beds</u>.
Mom <u>cleans</u> the house.
We all help with the <u>cooking</u>.
Dad <u>washes</u> the <u>dishes</u>.
When they are <u>washed</u>, we all watch TV.

Each underlined word is a root word with
an ending.

1. Tell what the root word and ending
   in each word is.

   You could write the root words and
   endings like this.

   work s

100

Too Much Talk
A Jataka Tale

Turtle lived in a small pond.
He liked to splash.
He liked to swim.

Best of all Turtle liked talking to
his friends.
One friend was Duck.
The other friend was Goose.

One day Goose said, "There is a
little pond over the mountain.
Duck and I want to live there."

"Please don't leave," said Turtle.

"Goose wishes you could go.
  And I do too," said Duck.

"But I can't go," said Turtle.
"You will be flying.
  I don't have wings."

"We will carry you," said Goose.
"Just hold onto this stick with
  your mouth."

"You must hold on tightly," said Duck.
"You can't talk when we fly."

Turtle wanted to go very much.
So he said, "I won't talk."

104

Goose took hold of one end of the stick.
Duck took hold of the other end.
Turtle took hold of the middle.
Then the three went up.

Soon Turtle looked down.
He saw a big lake.

"Let's stop here," said Turtle.

Down went Turtle.
He landed in the lake.
Duck and Goose just flew on.

Turtle had a new home.
But he had lost two friends.
Turtle had learned a lesson.

Sometimes even a little talk
is too much.

Think about the selection

1. Why did Turtle fall into the lake?
2. Could this story have happened?
   How do you know?

Checkpoint 8

Turtle missed his old home.
Now he swims alone.
Turtle is learning to like the lake.
But he wishes he had friends.

1. What is the root word in *missed*?
2. What ending was added to it?
3. What is the root word in *swims*?
4. What ending was added to it?
5. What is the root word in *learning*?
6. What ending was added to it?
7. What is the root word in *wishes*?
8. What ending was added to it?

8: Assess

Kites, Bikes, and a Race

Jim's kite has a long tail.
Ann's kite has a longer tail.
Judy's kite has the longest
tail of all.
None of the kites has a short tail.

Think about skills

The opposite of *short* is *long.*

The root word in *longer* is *long.*
The ending added to *long* was *er.*

The root word in *longest* is *long.*
The ending added to *long* was *est.*

9: Teach

Lola was not slow.
She ran fast.
But Mary ran faster.
Wendy ran the fastest of all.
Wendy won the race.

1. Did the tallest or the shortest girl
   win the race?
2. What word means the opposite of *slow?*
3. What is the root word in *faster?*
4. What ending was added to *fast* in *faster?*
5. What is the root word in *fastest?*
6. What ending was added to *fast* in *fastest?*

9: Teach

Practice skills

Lib's bike has small wheels.
Pedro's bike has smaller wheels.
Jack's bike has the smallest wheels of all.
None of the bikes is big.

1. What word means the opposite
   of *big?*
2. What is the root word in *smaller?*
3. What ending was added to *small*
   in *smaller?*
4. What ending was added to *small*
   in *smallest?*

My Friend Chip

Chip is my dog.
Chip likes to run.
But he is not the fastest dog.

9: Apply

The fastest dog belongs to Pam.
Pam's dog runs faster than Chip.

9: Apply

Chip is not the slowest dog.

The slowest dog belongs to Mike.
Mike's dog runs slower than Chip.

Chip does not run too fast.
He does not run too slow.
Chip runs just fast enough for me.

Chip is not as big as Pam's dog.
Chip is not as small as Mike's dog.
Chip is just the right size for me.

When Chip's tail wags, he is happy.
When I am happy, Chip is happy too.

When I am not happy, Chip knows
what to do.
He comes and sits next to me.
Then he puts his head on my arm.
He always makes me feel good.

118

Think about the selection

1. How does Chip show he is happy?
2. Can Chip tell when his owner is not happy? How do you know?

Checkpoint 9

1. What is the root word in *fastest?*
2. What is the root word in *smaller?*
3. What ending was added to *short* in *shorter?*
4. Which word means the opposite of *slowest?*

   longest   fastest
5. Which is the smallest dog?

a   b   c

Fun with Clowns

Jojo is funny.
<u>He</u> has big feet.

Look at the underlined word.
<u>He</u> stands for Jojo.

Dolly is smart.
<u>She</u> does a trick.

Look at the underlined word.
<u>She</u> stands for Dolly.

Jojo and Dolly are clowns.
<u>They</u> make the children laugh.

1. Who does <u>they</u> stand for?
   the clowns   the children

10: Teach

The clowns will be
in a parade.
It will go downtown.

2. What does it stand for?
   downtown   a parade

Practice skills

What does each underlined word stand for?

1. Jojo falls over his big feet.
   He picks himself up.
   feet   Jojo
2. No one can find Dolly.
   She is hiding behind Jojo.
   Dolly   Jojo
3. The band played for the parade.
   It played happy music.
   the music   the band   the parade
4. The children clapped and clapped.
   They liked the clowns and the music.
   the clowns   the music   the children

THE SILENT CLOWNS

Who wants to be a clown?
These people do.
So they put on funny faces.
And they become clowns.

10: Apply

The clowns never say a word.
But they have fun.

Sometimes people stop.
Sometimes they smile.

The clowns wait for a bus.
They will take the bus to
the park.
They want to find more people.

124

The clowns find children
at the park.
One clown pretends she
can't find two children.

Another clown pretends
he can't pull
some children.

One clown holds a baby.
Then the clown dances with
a child.

All the people at the park have
a good time.
The clowns do too.

126

Think about the selection

1. Why did the clowns go to the park?
2. What did the clowns do first?
   next? last?
   a. They went to the park.
   b. They put on funny faces.
   c. They took a bus.

Checkpoint 10

The clowns had to go home.
But *they* wanted to stay with the people.

1. Does *they* stand for the clowns or the people?

One boy asked a clown to stay.
He wanted to play some more.

2. Does *he* stand for the clown or the boy?

A girl asked a clown to stay too.
She wanted to laugh and dance.

3. Does *she* stand for the girl or the clown?

Shoes for Clowns

These people make shoes for clowns.
They work in their home.

This is John, the clown shoemaker.
One day a clown came to the door.
The clown needed new shoes.
She wanted shoes that were big and bright.

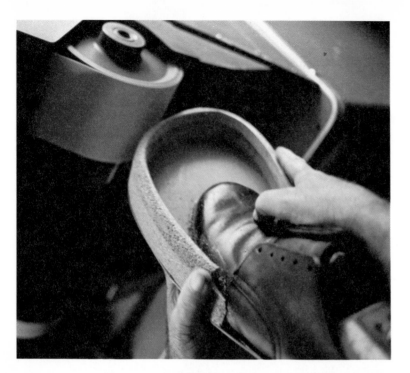

One shoemaker
cut wood.
The wood was
put on
each shoe.
This made the
shoes look big.

One shoemaker
made a red cover
for the wood.
This made the
shoes look bright.

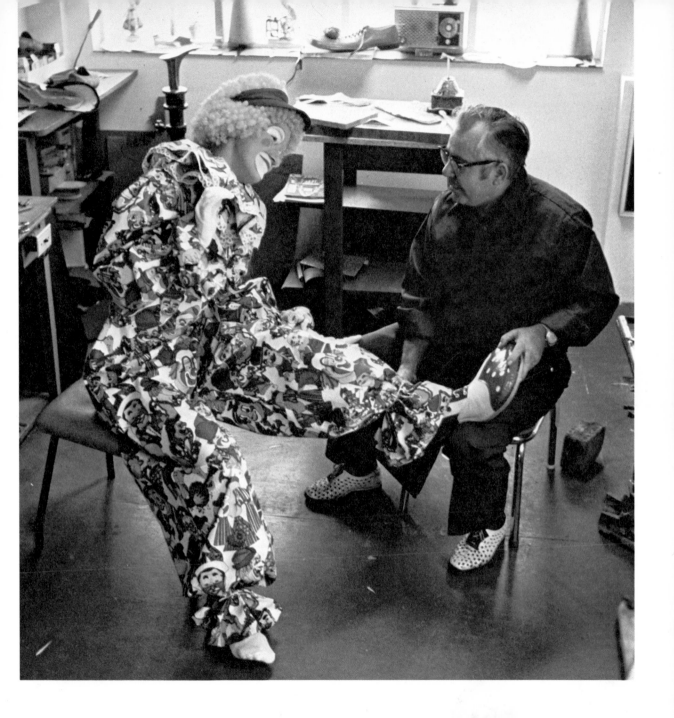

When the shoes were made, the clown tried
one on.
It looked big. It looked bright.

"This shoe
is just right
for me," said
the clown.

Think about the selection

1. What did one clown shoemaker cut and put on each shoe?
2. What did one clown shoemaker put over the wood?

How to Make a Clown Pencil-Holder

You will need these things.

paper

scissors

crayons

a small empty milk carton

tape

133

First wash out the milk carton.
Let it dry.

Next cut a circle out of paper.

Draw a clown's face on it.

Cut out a hat for your clown.

Color the hat.

Tape the hat on the clown's head.

Turn the open side
of the milk carton
away from you.
The face will go
on the side
nearest you.

Tape the clown to the
side of the carton.

Now you have a pencil-holder.

Think about the selection

1. Which parts will make a clown pencil-holder?

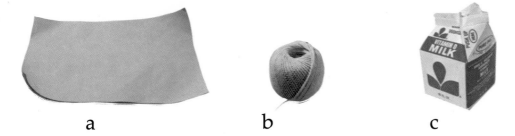

a   b   c

2. To make a clown pencil-holder what do you do first? next? last?
   a. Cut a circle out of paper.
   b. Tape the clown to the side of the carton.
   c. Wash out a milk carton.

3. What makes the hat stick to the clown's head?

a   b   c

11

Vowels

The Elf

An elf had animals to feed.
Eve the goat ate cheese.
The sheep liked her grass.
Fresh cream would
please Bea.
The elf had geese named
Bert and Deane.
These geese wanted to
eat ferns.
But the elf chased them.

Think about skills

» A vowel letter stands for more than
one sound.
Two vowel letters together usually
stand for one sound. «

Words like *elf* and *fresh* usually have
a short vowel sound.
Words like *her* and *ferns* usually have
an r-controlled vowel sound.
Words like *these, eat, please, feed,* and
cheese usually have a long vowel sound.

You saw these words in the story.

them   sheep   Deane   cream
Bea   Bert   geese   Eve

1. Which words have long vowel sounds?
2. Which word has a short vowel sound?
3. Which word has an r-controlled vowel sound?

Practice skills

The elf sat by a <u>stream</u>.
There was a nice <u>breeze</u>.
He saw a fox and <u>her</u> cubs.
He tried to <u>breathe</u> quietly.
But the foxes <u>went</u> away.

1. Which underlined words have long vowel sounds?
2. Which word has a short vowel sound?
3. Which word has an r-controlled sound?

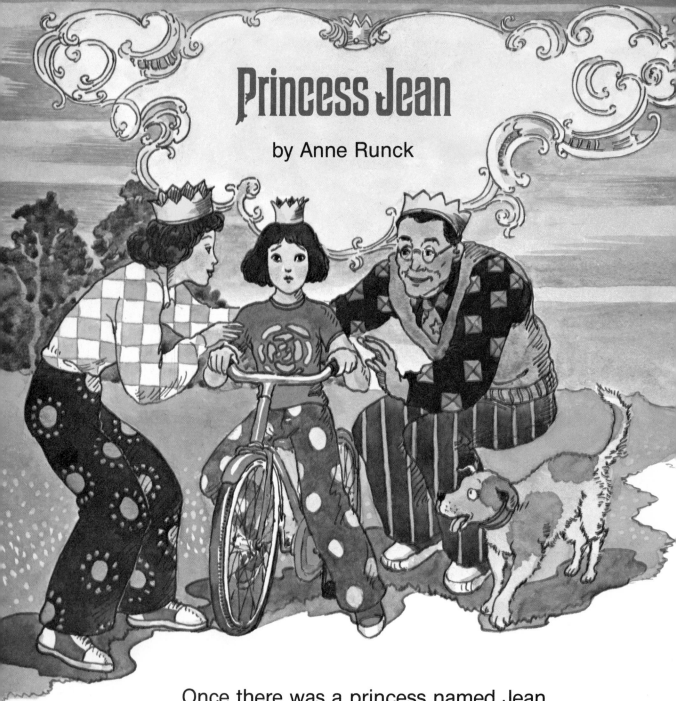

Princess Jean

by Anne Runck

Once there was a princess named Jean.
She liked to do things by herself.
But it was hard.
The king and queen always tried to help her.

140

Jean tried to climb a tree in the yard.

The queen said, "Please let me help you."
The queen gave Jean a ladder.

Jean tried to skate.

The king said, "Please let me help you.
I'll hold your hand. I'll teach you to skate."

All that help made Jean mad.

"I want to do something all by myself,"
she said.
"I'll make a kite and fly it."

So Jean got these things.
She got some paper, sticks, paste, rags, and
some string.

142

The king and the queen said, "Please let us help you."

Jean said, "No, thank you.
I can make the kite myself."

And she did. Jean made a beautiful kite.

Jean said, "Now I'll fly my kite."

The king and the queen said, "Please let us help you."

Jean said, "No, thank you.
I can fly it myself."

Jean got her skates.
Then she went to the top of the castle.
She skated around the roof of the castle.

Jean felt the breeze take the kite up.
The kite went up and up and up.
It went far, far up.

"There," said Jean. "At last I did something all by myself."

11: Apply

Think about the selection

1. What did Jean make with paper, sticks, paste, rags, and string?

   a tree   a ladder   a kite

2. What made the kite go up?

   the skates   the breeze   the roof

Checkpoint 11 ▮▭▭▭▭▭▭▭▭

Jean took her kite to the beach.
The king and queen went too.
Jean said, "Please help me fly my kite."

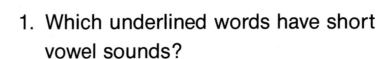

1. Which underlined words have short vowel sounds?

2. Which underlined words have long vowel sounds?

3. Which underlined word has an r-controlled vowel sound?

11: Assess

My Kite

by Myra Cohn Livingston

Bonus
Selection

It was splendid,
My kite—
It flew and it flew
When we let out the string
In the wind,
And we knew
    It would fly with the birds—
    It would fly to the sea—

Then its tail
Tangled up in a
Terrible tree.

From *The Moon and a Star*, copyright ©
1965 by Myra Cohn Livingston.
Reprinted by permission of Harcourt
Brace Jovanovich, Inc.

147

Buff and the School Bus

The school bus came.
Julie got on. Julie's dog, Buff, did too.
The driver saw Buff. Buff had to get off.

Think about skills

The main idea in a story is what the story
is all about.

The main idea in this story is
dogs can't ride on a school bus.

148

Julie fed Buff.
She gave him water.
She played with him.
Julie took care of Buff.

1. What is the main idea in this story?

Julie had a birthday party.
There was ice cream.
There was a big cake.
It had six candles.

1. What is the main idea in this story?

I Love You, Mary Jane

by Lorna Balian

Today is Mary Jane's birthday party.
Don't forget.

From *I Love You, Mary Jane* by Lorna Balian. Copyright © 1967 by
Abingdon Press. Reprinted by permission of Abingdon Press.

12: Apply

152

154

Think about the selection

1. What is Mary Jane?
2. What did Mary Jane give each child?
3. What presents did the children bring Mary Jane?

Checkpoint 12 ▬▬▬▬▬▬▬▬

1. What is the main idea in the story?
   a. Someone gave Mary Jane a ribbon.
   b. Some children had a party for a dog.
   c. One child brought Mary Jane a fish.

Section Two Checkpoint

Word Identification Tests

Subtest 1

long	3. r-controlled
ⓐ pet ⓑ help ⓒ please ⓓ DK	ⓐ her ⓑ men ⓒ tree ⓓ DK
1. short	4. long
ⓐ eat ⓑ fell ⓒ queen ⓓ DK	ⓐ bench ⓑ bed ⓒ cream ⓓ DK
2. long	5. long
ⓐ sheep ⓑ spell ⓒ went ⓓ DK	ⓐ next ⓑ week ⓒ let ⓓ DK

stop

Subtest 2

ⓐ child ⓑ mothers ⓒ father ⓓ DK	8. ⓐ washes ⓑ around ⓒ house ⓓ DK
6. ⓐ slowest ⓑ friend ⓒ last ⓓ DK	9. ⓐ lettuce ⓑ middle ⓒ longer ⓓ DK
7. ⓐ whose ⓑ looked ⓒ sandwich ⓓ DK	10. ⓐ bring ⓑ going ⓒ thing ⓓ DK

stop

Subtest 3

11.	ⓐ balloon	ⓑ bigger	
	ⓒ bright	ⓓ DK	
15.	ⓐ pencil	ⓑ party	
	ⓒ parade	ⓓ DK	

11. ⓐ balloon ⓑ bigger ⓒ bright ⓓ DK
15. ⓐ pencil ⓑ party ⓒ parade ⓓ DK

12. ⓐ into ⓑ short ⓒ idea ⓓ DK
16. ⓐ read ⓑ ranch ⓒ rope ⓓ DK

13. ⓐ long ⓑ list ⓒ love ⓓ DK
17. ⓐ slow ⓑ shoe ⓒ school ⓓ DK

14. ⓐ machine ⓑ mail ⓒ myself ⓓ DK
18. ⓐ who ⓑ would ⓒ work ⓓ DK

Possible Word Identification Score: 18   **stop**

Comprehension Tests

Subtest 4

1. *To leave* means
  ⓐ to stay
  ⓑ to go
  ⓒ DK

3. The word *usually* means
  ⓐ most of the time
  ⓑ all of the time
  ⓒ DK

2. A *breeze* is a
  ⓐ soft wind
  ⓑ strong wind
  ⓒ DK

4. The word *each* means
  ⓐ some
  ⓑ every one
  ⓒ DK

stop

Subtest 5

Wendy, Steve, Bruce, and
Jean went to a parade.
Dad and Mom took *them*.

5. Who does *them* stand for?
   ⓐ Dad and Mom
   ⓑ Wendy, Steve, Bruce,
      and Jean
   ⓒ DK

Bruce bought some popcorn.
He gave some to Steve.

6. Who does *he* stand for?
   ⓐ Bruce
   ⓑ Steve
   ⓒ DK

Wendy gave Jean a
balloon to hold.
She let it fly away.

7. Who does *she* stand for?
   ⓐ Jean
   ⓑ Wendy
   ⓒ DK

stop

Sako tries to feed herself.
Sometimes she misses her mouth.
Then the food gets on her face.
But Sako is doing better.
Now she gets more food in
her mouth.

8. What is the main idea in
   this story?
   ⓐ Sometimes Sako misses her mouth.
   ⓑ Sako is learning to feed herself.
   ⓒ Food gets on Sako's face.
   ⓓ DK

Ann likes to skate. Jim does too.
Jim likes to climb trees. Ann does too.
They have fun together.

9. What is the main idea in
   this story?
   ⓐ Ann and Jim like to skate.
   ⓑ Ann and Jim like to climb trees.
   ⓒ Ann and Jim like the same things.
   ⓓ DK

stop

Lupe liked to read.
But her eyes got tired.
Then Lupe got some glasses.
Now her eyes don't get tired.

10. Why don't Lupe's eyes get
    tired now?
    ⓐ She doesn't read now.
    ⓑ She found a new book.
    ⓒ She got some glasses.
    ⓓ DK

Jack was not happy.
He wanted to help bake cookies.
His sister said, "Boys can't cook."
His mother said, "Oh, yes they can."
So Jack helped bake cookies.
Then he was happy.

11. Why is Jack happy now?
    ⓐ He didn't like to bake cookies.
    ⓑ He helped bake cookies.
    ⓒ His sister liked to bake cookies.
    ⓓ DK

Possible Comprehension Score: 11   stop

Glossary

A a

ape An ape is a big monkey. Apes do not have tails.

arm Your arm is between your shoulder and hand. You have two arms.

B b

baby A baby is a very young child. Little babies can't walk.

bag You put things in a bag. Big bags can hold many things.

basket A basket holds things. Some baskets are big. Some are little.

bench A bench is a place to sit. Some benches are made of wood.

C c

calendar A calendar shows the months, weeks, and days of the year. Some calendars have pictures.

carton A carton is made of heavy paper. Some cartons hold milk.

circle A circle is round. It is not easy to draw perfect circles.

cut Uncle Lee cut the meat. He is cutting a piece for me. He has cut one for you too.

D d

dirt The shovel moves a pile of dirt.

draw The girl likes to draw. She is drawing a picture. She drew a house and trees.

drum A drum makes a loud noise when you hit it. You can hit drums with sticks or your hands.

169

H h

hit He hit the ball. He is hitting it hard. Once he hit it across the street.

M m

mail carrier A mail carrier delivers mail. Mail carriers bring letters from the post office.

mark Mark off the days on the big calendar. Keep marking off the days. You marked off only two days.

mountain A mountain is a very high hill. Some mountains have snow on top even in summer.

170

mouth Your mouth is in your head.
You eat and talk with your mouth.

P p

post office You can mail a letter
at a post office. Mail carriers
bring mail from post offices.

pound The woman likes to pound with
a hammer. She is pounding a nail.
She pounded it hard.

pull The dog can pull the wagon.
He was pulling it all day. He
pulled the wagon home.

171

R r

remember It is nice to remember your birthday. This boy is remembering his. He remembered his birthday cake.

ribbon The girl has a blue ribbon. Ribbons look pretty on presents.

S s

scissors You can cut paper with scissors.

shoemaker A shoemaker makes shoes. Shoemakers fix shoes too.

size These boots are the right
size. Boots come in many sizes.

skate The boy is learning to skate.
He is skating on ice. He skated
on one foot.

smile The girl likes to smile. She
was smiling for her picture. The
frog smiled too.

surprise The girl gave her friend a
surprise. Some surprises are
very nice.

T t

tail A tail is part of an animal's body. Kites have tails too.

tape The man has some tape. He uses tape to fix books.

U u

umbrella An umbrella keeps the rain off your head. Umbrellas can be many colors.

W w

wheel A wheel is round. Wagons and cars have four wheels.

Word List

The following high-frequency words (words that appear on recognized word lists) have been read enough times in this and previous pupils' texts in *Basics in Reading* to reach mastery by the end of this book. Pupils will be able to recognize both the root word and the root word with these endings: *s, es, ed, ing, 's, er, est.*

    The page number printed after each word shows the first appearance in this book. For a cumulative list of high-frequency words see the Teacher's Edition for *Calico Caper*.

airplane 22	dad 11	just 36	pick 21
apple 34	dance 64		pot 49
	don't 15	let 22	
baby 84	draw 134	list 10	queen 140
back 22	dry 86	long 57	
balloon 33		love 150	rag 142
bigger 45	fast 46		ranch 17
book 8	flag 8	machine 35	read 16
bread 32	fly 22	mail 88	rock 58
bright 129	forget 150	many 18	rope 20
bring 16	from 29	me 9	
	fun 74	milk 56	say 31
cake 16		more 21	school 56
call 20	grandmother 22	music 121	sentence 22
can't 22	grandpa 98	myself 142	shoe 128
care 18			short 57
cattle 17	him 12	no 65	slide 46
child 55	hold 15		slow 110
circle 8	horse 22	or 110	small 35
clown 120			sometimes 20
cold 43	idea 89	parade 121	spell 65
color 135	into 13	party 149	stand 8
cow 22		pencil 133	stay 31
cut 130		pet 65	

stick 34

swim 42

tail 109

tall 110

them 11

time 43

took 13

truck 21

turn 66

use 20

watch 8

week 90

wet 43

wheel 66

when 16

who 29

woman 21

work 21

would 30

your 11

A separate group of words considered technical in this program appears below. Pupils will be able to recognize these terms.

consonant 8

ending 99

main idea 148

opposite 109

r-controlled 57

root word 99

selection 16

vowel 56